The Daily

a ritual to set the
tone of your day and life

The Daily

a ritual to set the
tone of your day and life

Created by Jill Wintersteen

SPIRIT DAUGHTER PUBLISHING

for the believers in magic, the
energy shifters, and the ones
who align with the power of the
universe -

thank you for your commitment
to changing yourself and
the world.

a note from jill

The journey you are about to begin with this book is one that can continue for the rest of your life. It has the potential to become the foundation of your every intention, every hope, and every dream. If you allow it, this practice will see you through decades of change as you grow and evolve into the person you are meant to be in this life.

I began doing this practice every morning sixteen years ago. I was twenty-five at the time. It has seen me through the birth of my child, my decision to get married (twice), and the creation of my company. It led to dozens of plane tickets purchased and thousands of miles traveled. It's my anchor when the world feels overwhelming or when my emotions feel chaotic. It bridges the seeds I plant each New Moon with the work I do on the Full Moon to manifest those dreams.

Each day, I wake before the rest of the house, and I sit to meditate. Afterward, I take out my notebook and do this practice. I have piles of notebooks full of simple gratitudes, the 5/5 list, and daily mantras. I look back through them from time to time to remind myself of what I've wanted throughout the years and how my life has evolved. I see which dreams persisted and which were fleeting whims. I can witness the cycle of my changing days from a young yoga teacher to a mother, wife, and business owner. It's all there, in stacks of journals preserving a lifetime of daily lists.

I decided to create this journal as an offering to you. This is my personal practice, and I want to give it to anyone willing to try it. It's simple. So simple, you may not believe its power. I can tell you, though, this practice, when continuously done, will change your life in ways you can't even imagine. Its magic is subtle. You'll barely notice it until you look back years later and see that everything has changed. Then you, too, will have piles of journals that serve as a record of your evolving self.

Enjoy this time to sit each day and learn who you are and what you want. You may just surprise yourself. I know I have.

xoxo
Jill

why

Daily routines have been shown to improve overall life satisfaction. They improve health, sleep, relationships, and stress levels. Routines simply make us happy. We are creatures of habit. When we commit to doing something each day, no matter where we are, what's happening to us emotionally, or what's occurring in the world, our lives improve. We feel good, and that positive vibration affects everyone we come into contact with and improves our ability to manifest the life of our dreams. When we are in a good mood, we attract energy that helps us stay in that feeling. A daily routine becomes the cornerstone we build our visions around.

When we practice a routine in the morning, our day changes. We are less forgetful, more productive, and more confident in ourselves. We feel in control of our lives, and we know what to do next. We can visualize our day and have the courage to say no to anything that does not align with our vision. A routine in the morning also can lower stress levels and give us space before the day's tasks begin. It provides a moment of peace when we know what to expect and what will happen. This peace extends to the rest of our day, reminding us that we can always give ourselves a bit of space when we need it.

As for nighttime routines, they give us closure to our day and help us sleep more soundly. Evening rituals tell our body it's time to wind down and rest. Even babies sleep better when they have a consistent nighttime routine. Routines do not need to be elaborate to work. Simple practices can become a cue to your body that it's time to end the day and take a break before a new one begins.

So why do a daily practice? To sum it up: better sleep, less brain fog, more confidence, abundant positive vibrations, and inner peace. It seems like a good reason to make it a habit. Luckily, you get all these benefits in a matter of moments with this book if you allow it into your life.

How

The best part about this book is it's easy to use. It asks for only about five minutes of your day and can be done anywhere. You can do this practice by itself or add it after a meditation session. It's suggested, though, that you feel at peace in your energy and calm in your mind before beginning. This practice does have the ability to ground you. So if you need to do it during a busy day, that works too.

The practice begins with a gratitude list. Write three to ten things you are grateful for right now. This list can include people in your life, your abundance, your gifts, your life path, your health, your home, and so much more. Notice if you begin to write the same things each day and challenge yourself to switch it up a bit. There is so much to be grateful for in this life. You may be surprised at the things you can come up with when you expand your vision. If you are going through a challenging time and find it hard to be grateful for anything, you always have your breath to thank. Start there and allow your heart to open to all the good in your life.

The 5/5 list is the core exercise of this practice. Begin by writing five things you need to do today on the list to the left. Even if you have more to do on a certain day, pick the most important items. Your mind will remember these throughout the day and will make them a priority. You will also find that after setting this to-do list, the rest of your day becomes clear. Your time will form around your list of five, and everything else will fall into place. Also, remember to work in to-do items like rest or enjoy life. These little reminders will go a long way in lowering your stress level and bringing joy into your world.

The daily to-do list can inform you about how you feel about your life right now. Notice how you respond to the list each day. Does it excite you? Bore you? How do you feel about the things you need to do each day? If you find yourself underwhelmed by your daily life, it may be time to change things around. What we do each day adds up to a life. Make sure you enjoy and look forward to a good portion of your to-do list. If you feel less than content, add plans to create some changes so that you feel fulfilled and excited by your daily life.

On the list to the right, write five things you want to do in your life at any time. This is where you dream. Unrestrict yourself here and reach for the stars. Items on this list can be things like travel to Egypt, start a company, write a book, sail the Caribbean, or anything else you can envision. Challenge yourself to dig deep and find your true desires. Even if they feel impossible or silly, write them down and see if they stick.

As you continue to do this practice, some things will show up over and over on this dream list, while other items will be fleeting wishes. As you look back on days and months of your dreams, you will see that the ones that truly resonate with your soul repeat themselves through time. These are the dreams you build intentions around each month. Perhaps some of the steps to manifest them make their way to your to-do list, changing your daily life. This practice of writing down your dreams helps you focus your energy on what's most important and what the soul desires. Done consistently, this "dream" list can help decide some of the most important decisions of your life.

Once you've written the 5/5 list, then it's time to write a mantra for the day. Create a powerful "I am" statement that will help you navigate your day and even manifest your dreams. This mantra can stay the same for a while or change every day. Let your intuition guide you in creating it, and return to it throughout the day to help remain clear in your mind and energy.

The last part of this practice happens in the evening, at the end of your day. These questions help you reflect on the day and find some joy in it. It reminds you to be thankful for the day and perceive special moments you may have forgotten. This portion also reminds you to be excited for the next day, helping get you out of bed the following morning. Again, if you are having trouble finding something to get excited about, it may be time to make some changes. Do this nightly practice to conclude the day with ceremony, reference, and appreciation for what is.

when

This practice is best done in the morning, first thing when you wake up if possible. We each have different responsibilities in the morning, which will change with life. You may find yourself getting out of bed each day to do this practice for a few years. Then you may need to shift to doing it after your children are off to school or the dog is walked. You can choose to do it whenever it suits your life best, but the earlier, the better. It gives clarity and joy to your day. And who doesn't want that at the start of each day?

For the nighttime questions, you can answer those whenever you feel your day is complete. You might do this practice at dinner time and make it a shared experience with loved ones, or you may choose to answer these questions before bed as a way to signal to your body that you are ready to rest.

Whenever you decide to complete the morning and the evening practices, try to be consistent. Our energy is a creature of habit, and when we do a routine at the same time each day, it grows to expect it and prepare for it. By doing a practice at the same time each day, we allow our energy to learn the rhythm of our life and show up fully for the event.

where

The best thing about this practice is you can do it anywhere. You can do it in bed. You can do it at the kitchen table. You can even do it on the train to work. The most important thing is that you feel at ease where you practice and that it's quiet enough to hear your thoughts. It's also beneficial to feel comfortable when practicing, feeling supported by the chair, floor, or Earth below you.

what
to expect

Magic

Clarity throughout your day

Clear visions of the future

Inner knowing of where to place your energy

Joy in your heart

Manifestation of your dreams

for example

3 | 26 | 21

i am grateful for:

My home & the calming energy it brings.
The work I am able to do every day (creating all day ♥)
A body that brings me hiking/running/yoga-ing
Nature & living so close to the forest/mountains
All the beautiful humans I call friends
My kitty... & all the love + playfulness she provides

5 things i need to do today

1 Finish moon illustration
2 Send in my taxes...
3 Email Emma back
4 Buy birthday gift for Allie
5 Practice piano

5 things i want to do in my life

1 Go to Morrocco
2 Go on a meditation retreat
3 Split my time // live in 2 places
4 Play music consistently
5 Scuba dive around the world

today's mantra

I am a powerful & healing voice.

– PM –

this made me smile today:

An old video a friend sent of her & I dancing
in Hey Arnold costumes ha

what i'm looking forward to tomorrow:

Drawing all day long & a trail run ♥

you have two choices:

- settle for what's comfortable

- have the courage to grow
  into the unknown

you can't have both.

date

—— | —— | ——

i am grateful for:

_____

_____

_____

_____

_____

_____

5 things i need to do today

1 _____
2 _____
3 _____
4 _____
5 _____

5 things i want to do in my life

1 _____
2 _____
3 _____
4 _____
5 _____

today's mantra

_____

this made me smile today:

_____

what i'm looking forward to tomorrow:

_____

date

—— | —— | ——

i am grateful for:

_____

_____

_____

_____

_____

_____

5 things i need to do today

1 _____

2 _____

3 _____

4 _____

5 _____

5 things i want to do in my life

1 _____

2 _____

3 _____

4 _____

5 _____

today's mantra

_____

this made me smile today:

_____

what i'm looking forward to tomorrow:

_____

date

—— | —— | ——

i am grateful for:

_____

_____

_____

_____

_____

_____

5 things i need to do today

1 _____

2 _____

3 _____

4 _____

5 _____

5 things i want to do in my life

1 _____

2 _____

3 _____

4 _____

5 _____

today's mantra

_____

this made me smile today:

_____

what i'm looking forward to tomorrow:

_____

i am grateful for:

_____

_____

_____

_____

_____

_____

5 things i need to do today

1 _____

2 _____

3 _____

4 _____

5 _____

5 things i want to do in my life

1 _____

2 _____

3 _____

4 _____

5 _____

today's mantra

_____

this made me smile today:

_____

what i'm looking forward to tomorrow:

_____

i am grateful for:

_____

_____

_____

_____

_____

5 things i need to do today   *5 things i want to do in my life*

1 _____   1 _____

2 _____   2 _____

3 _____   3 _____

4 _____   4 _____

5 _____   5 _____

today's mantra

_____

this made me smile today:

_____

what i'm looking forward to tomorrow:

_____

date

— | — | —

i am grateful for:

_____

_____

_____

_____

_____

_____

5 things i need to do today   *5 things i want to do in my life*

1 _____   1 _____

2 _____   2 _____

3 _____   3 _____

4 _____   4 _____

5 _____   5 _____

today's mantra

_____

this made me smile today:

_____

what i'm looking forward to tomorrow:

_____

date

___ | ___ | ___

i am grateful for:

_____

_____

_____

_____

_____

_____

5 things i need to do today

1 _____

2 _____

3 _____

4 _____

5 _____

5 things i want to do in my life

1 _____

2 _____

3 _____

4 _____

5 _____

today's mantra

_____

this made me smile today:

_____

what i'm looking forward to tomorrow:

_____

date

—— | —— | ——

i am grateful for:

_____

_____

_____

_____

_____

_____

_____

5 things i need to do today

1 _____

2 _____

3 _____

4 _____

5 _____

5 things i want to do in my life

1 _____

2 _____

3 _____

4 _____

5 _____

today's mantra

_____

this made me smile today:

_____

what i'm looking forward to tomorrow:

_____

date

—— | —— | ——

i am grateful for:

_____

_____

_____

_____

_____

_____

5 things i need to do today	*5 things i want to do in my life*
1 _____	1 _____
2 _____	2 _____
3 _____	3 _____
4 _____	4 _____
5 _____	5 _____

today's mantra

_____

this made me smile today:

_____

what i'm looking forward to tomorrow:

_____

date

—— | —— | ——

i am grateful for:

_____

_____

_____

_____

_____

_____

5 things i need to do today	*5 things i want to do in my life*
1	1
2	2
3	3
4	4
5	5

today's mantra

_____

this made me smile today:

_____

what i'm looking forward to tomorrow:

_____

—— | —— | ——

i am grateful for:

_____

_____

_____

_____

_____

_____

5 things i need to do today   *5 things i want to do in my life*

1 _____   1 _____

2 _____   2 _____

3 _____   3 _____

4 _____   4 _____

5 _____   5 _____

today's mantra

_____

this made me smile today:

_____

what i'm looking forward to tomorrow:

_____

date

—— | —— | ——

i am grateful for:

_____

_____

_____

_____

_____

_____

5 things i need to do today

1 _____

2 _____

3 _____

4 _____

5 _____

5 things i want to do in my life

1 _____

2 _____

3 _____

4 _____

5 _____

today's mantra

_____

this made me smile today:

_____

what i'm looking forward to tomorrow:

_____

date

___ | ___ | ___

i am grateful for:

_____

_____

_____

_____

_____

_____

_____

5 things i need to do today   *5 things i want to do in my life*

1 _____   1 _____

2 _____   2 _____

3 _____   3 _____

4 _____   4 _____

5 _____   5 _____

today's mantra

_____

this made me smile today:

_____

what i'm looking forward to tomorrow:

_____

date

— | — | —

i am grateful for:

_____

_____

_____

_____

_____

_____

5 things i need to do today

1 _____

2 _____

3 _____

4 _____

5 _____

5 things i want to do in my life

1 _____

2 _____

3 _____

4 _____

5 _____

today's mantra

_____

this made me smile today:

_____

what i'm looking forward to tomorrow:

_____

date

—— | —— | ——

i am grateful for:

_____

_____

_____

_____

_____

5 things i need to do today

1 _____

2 _____

3 _____

4 _____

5 _____

5 things i want to do in my life

1 _____

2 _____

3 _____

4 _____

5 _____

today's mantra

_____

this made me smile today:

_____

what i'm looking forward to tomorrow:

_____

date

—— | —— | ——

i am grateful for:

_____

_____

_____

_____

_____

_____

5 things i need to do today   *5 things i want to do in my life*

1 _____   1 _____

2 _____   2 _____

3 _____   3 _____

4 _____   4 _____

5 _____   5 _____

today's mantra

_____

this made me smile today:

_____

what i'm looking forward to tomorrow:

_____

date

—— | —— | ——

i am grateful for:

_____

_____

_____

_____

_____

_____

5 things i need to do today	*5 things i want to do in my life*
1 _____	1 _____
2 _____	2 _____
3 _____	3 _____
4 _____	4 _____
5 _____	5 _____

today's mantra

_____

this made me smile today:

_____

what i'm looking forward to tomorrow:

_____

date

—— | —— | ——

i am grateful for:

_____

_____

_____

_____

_____

_____

5 things i need to do today   *5 things i want to do in my life*

1 _____   1 _____

2 _____   2 _____

3 _____   3 _____

4 _____   4 _____

5 _____   5 _____

today's mantra

_____

this made me smile today:

_____

what i'm looking forward to tomorrow:

_____

39

date

— | — | —

i am grateful for:

_____

_____

_____

_____

_____

_____

5 things i need to do today

1 _____

2 _____

3 _____

4 _____

5 _____

5 things i want to do in my life

1 _____

2 _____

3 _____

4 _____

5 _____

today's mantra

_____

this made me smile today:

_____

what i'm looking forward to tomorrow:

_____

date

—— | —— | ——

i am grateful for:

_____

_____

_____

_____

_____

_____

5 things i need to do today   *5 things i want to do in my life*

1 _____   1 _____

2 _____   2 _____

3 _____   3 _____

4 _____   4 _____

5 _____   5 _____

today's mantra

_____

this made me smile today:

_____

what i'm looking forward to tomorrow:

_____

it's not a coincidence

it's a sign

•

trust it.

•

◉

date

___ | ___ | ___

i am grateful for:

_____

_____

_____

_____

_____

_____

5 things i need to do today

1 _____

2 _____

3 _____

4 _____

5 _____

5 things i want to do in my life

1 _____

2 _____

3 _____

4 _____

5 _____

today's mantra

_____

this made me smile today:

_____

what i'm looking forward to tomorrow:

_____

44

—— | —— | ——

i am grateful for:

_____

_____

_____

_____

_____

5 things i need to do today

1 _____

2 _____

3 _____

4 _____

5 _____

5 things i want to do in my life

1 _____

2 _____

3 _____

4 _____

5 _____

today's mantra

_____

this made me smile today:

_____

what i'm looking forward to tomorrow:

_____

i am grateful for:

_____

_____

_____

_____

_____

_____

5 things i need to do today

1 _____

2 _____

3 _____

4 _____

5 _____

5 things i want to do in my life

1 _____

2 _____

3 _____

4 _____

5 _____

today's mantra

_____

this made me smile today:

_____

what i'm looking forward to tomorrow:

_____

date

___ | ___ | ___

i am grateful for:

_____

_____

_____

_____

_____

_____

5 things i need to do today

1 _____

2 _____

3 _____

4 _____

5 _____

5 things i want to do in my life

1 _____

2 _____

3 _____

4 _____

5 _____

today's mantra

_____

this made me smile today:

_____

what i'm looking forward to tomorrow:

_____

date

—— | —— | ——

i am grateful for:

_____

_____

_____

_____

_____

_____

5 things i need to do today

1 _____

2 _____

3 _____

4 _____

5 _____

5 things i want to do in my life

1 _____

2 _____

3 _____

4 _____

5 _____

today's mantra

_____

this made me smile today:

_____

what i'm looking forward to tomorrow:

_____

date

—— | —— | ——

i am grateful for:

_____

_____

_____

_____

_____

_____

5 things i need to do today

1 _____

2 _____

3 _____

4 _____

5 _____

5 things i want to do in my life

1 _____

2 _____

3 _____

4 _____

5 _____

today's mantra

_____

this made me smile today:

_____

what i'm looking forward to tomorrow:

_____

___ | ___ | ___

i am grateful for:

_____

_____

_____

_____

_____

_____

5 things i need to do today

1 _____

2 _____

3 _____

4 _____

5 _____

5 things i want to do in my life

1 _____

2 _____

3 _____

4 _____

5 _____

today's mantra

_____

this made me smile today:

_____

what i'm looking forward to tomorrow:

_____

date

— | — | —

i am grateful for:

_____

_____

_____

_____

_____

_____

5 things i need to do today

1 _____

2 _____

3 _____

4 _____

5 _____

5 things i want to do in my life

1 _____

2 _____

3 _____

4 _____

5 _____

today's mantra

_____

this made me smile today:

_____

what i'm looking forward to tomorrow:

_____

date

___ | ___ | ___

i am grateful for:

_____

_____

_____

_____

_____

_____

5 things i need to do today

1 _____

2 _____

3 _____

4 _____

5 _____

5 things i want to do in my life

1 _____

2 _____

3 _____

4 _____

5 _____

today's mantra

_____

this made me smile today:

_____

what i'm looking forward to tomorrow:

_____

i am grateful for:

_____

_____

_____

_____

_____

_____

5 things i need to do today

1 _____

2 _____

3 _____

4 _____

5 _____

5 things i want to do in my life

1 _____

2 _____

3 _____

4 _____

5 _____

today's mantra

_____

this made me smile today:

_____

what i'm looking forward to tomorrow:

_____

date

___ | ___ | ___

i am grateful for:

_____

_____

_____

_____

_____

_____

5 things i need to do today	*5 things i want to do in my life*
1 _____	1 _____
2 _____	2 _____
3 _____	3 _____
4 _____	4 _____
5 _____	5 _____

today's mantra

_____

this made me smile today:

_____

what i'm looking forward to tomorrow:

_____

date

—— | —— | ——

i am grateful for:

_____

_____

_____

_____

_____

_____

5 things i need to do today

1 _____

2 _____

3 _____

4 _____

5 _____

5 things i want to do in my life

1 _____

2 _____

3 _____

4 _____

5 _____

today's mantra

_____

this made me smile today:

_____

what i'm looking forward to tomorrow:

_____

date

—— | —— | ——

i am grateful for:

_____

_____

_____

_____

_____

_____

5 things i need to do today	*5 things i want to do in my life*
1	1
2	2
3	3
4	4
5	5

today's mantra

_____

this made me smile today:

_____

what i'm looking forward to tomorrow:

_____

date

—— | —— | ——

i am grateful for:

_____

_____

_____

_____

_____

_____

5 things i need to do today

1 _____

2 _____

3 _____

4 _____

5 _____

5 things i want to do in my life

1 _____

2 _____

3 _____

4 _____

5 _____

today's mantra

_____

this made me smile today:

_____

what i'm looking forward to tomorrow:

_____

date

___ | ___ | ___

i am grateful for:

_____

_____

_____

_____

_____

_____

5 things i need to do today

1 _____

2 _____

3 _____

4 _____

5 _____

5 things i want to do in my life

1 _____

2 _____

3 _____

4 _____

5 _____

today's mantra

_____

this made me smile today:

_____

what i'm looking forward to tomorrow:

_____

date

___ | ___ | ___

i am grateful for:

_____

_____

_____

_____

_____

5 things i need to do today

1 _____

2 _____

3 _____

4 _____

5 _____

5 things i want to do in my life

1 _____

2 _____

3 _____

4 _____

5 _____

today's mantra

_____

this made me smile today:

_____

what i'm looking forward to tomorrow:

_____

date

___ | ___ | ___

i am grateful for:

_____

_____

_____

_____

_____

_____

5 things i need to do today

1 _____

2 _____

3 _____

4 _____

5 _____

5 things i want to do in my life

1 _____

2 _____

3 _____

4 _____

5 _____

today's mantra

_____

this made me smile today:

_____

what i'm looking forward to tomorrow:

_____

date

___ | ___ | ___

i am grateful for:

_____

_____

_____

_____

_____

_____

5 things i need to do today

1 _____

2 _____

3 _____

4 _____

5 _____

5 things i want to do in my life

1 _____

2 _____

3 _____

4 _____

5 _____

today's mantra

_____

this made me smile today:

_____

what i'm looking forward to tomorrow:

_____

— | — | —

i am grateful for:

_____

_____

_____

_____

_____

_____

5 things i need to do today

1 _____

2 _____

3 _____

4 _____

5 _____

5 things i want to do in my life

1 _____

2 _____

3 _____

4 _____

5 _____

today's mantra

_____

this made me smile today:

_____

what i'm looking forward to tomorrow:

_____

date

___ | ___ | ___

i am grateful for:

_____

_____

_____

_____

_____

_____

5 things i need to do today   *5 things i want to do in my life*

1 _____   1 _____

2 _____   2 _____

3 _____   3 _____

4 _____   4 _____

5 _____   5 _____

today's mantra

_____

this made me smile today:

_____

what i'm looking forward to tomorrow:

_____

attract what you need

don't chase and don't settle

trust that everything you

want is on its way to you.

___ | ___ | ___

i am grateful for:

_____

_____

_____

_____

_____

_____

5 things i need to do today   *5 things i want to do in my life*

1 _____   1 _____

2 _____   2 _____

3 _____   3 _____

4 _____   4 _____

5 _____   5 _____

today's mantra

_____

this made me smile today:

_____

what i'm looking forward to tomorrow:

_____

date

___ | ___ | ___

i am grateful for:

_____

_____

_____

_____

_____

_____

5 things i need to do today   *5 things i want to do in my life*

1 _____   1 _____

2 _____   2 _____

3 _____   3 _____

4 _____   4 _____

5 _____   5 _____

today's mantra

_____

this made me smile today:

_____

what i'm looking forward to tomorrow:

_____

date

___ | ___ | ___

i am grateful for:

_____

_____

_____

_____

_____

5 things i need to do today

1 _____

2 _____

3 _____

4 _____

5 _____

5 things i want to do in my life

1 _____

2 _____

3 _____

4 _____

5 _____

today's mantra

_____

this made me smile today:

_____

what i'm looking forward to tomorrow:

_____

date

___ | ___ | ___

i am grateful for:

_____

_____

_____

_____

_____

_____

5 things i need to do today   *5 things i want to do in my life*

1 _____   1 _____

2 _____   2 _____

3 _____   3 _____

4 _____   4 _____

5 _____   5 _____

today's mantra

_____

this made me smile today:

_____

what i'm looking forward to tomorrow:

_____

date

___ | ___ | ___

i am grateful for:

_____

_____

_____

_____

_____

_____

5 things i need to do today

1 _____

2 _____

3 _____

4 _____

5 _____

5 things i want to do in my life

1 _____

2 _____

3 _____

4 _____

5 _____

today's mantra

_____

this made me smile today:

_____

what i'm looking forward to tomorrow:

_____

___ | ___ | ___

i am grateful for:

_____

_____

_____

_____

_____

_____

5 things i need to do today   *5 things i want to do in my life*

1 _____   1 _____

2 _____   2 _____

3 _____   3 _____

4 _____   4 _____

5 _____   5 _____

today's mantra

_____

this made me smile today:

_____

what i'm looking forward to tomorrow:

_____

i am grateful for:

---

5 things i need to do today

1 _____
2 _____
3 _____
4 _____
5 _____

5 things i want to do in my life

1 _____
2 _____
3 _____
4 _____
5 _____

today's mantra

---

this made me smile today:

---

what i'm looking forward to tomorrow:

— | — | —

i am grateful for:

_____

_____

_____

_____

_____

_____

5 things i need to do today

1 _____

2 _____

3 _____

4 _____

5 _____

5 things i want to do in my life

1 _____

2 _____

3 _____

4 _____

5 _____

today's mantra

_____

this made me smile today:

_____

what i'm looking forward to tomorrow:

_____

date

— | — | —

i am grateful for:

_____

_____

_____

_____

_____

_____

5 things i need to do today

1 _____

2 _____

3 _____

4 _____

5 _____

5 things i want to do in my life

1 _____

2 _____

3 _____

4 _____

5 _____

today's mantra

_____

this made me smile today:

_____

what i'm looking forward to tomorrow:

_____

date

—— | —— | ——

i am grateful for:

_____

_____

_____

_____

_____

_____

5 things i need to do today	*5 things i want to do in my life*
1	1
2	2
3	3
4	4
5	5

today's mantra

_____

this made me smile today:

_____

what i'm looking forward to tomorrow:

_____

i am grateful for:

_____

_____

_____

_____

_____

_____

5 things i need to do today

1 _____

2 _____

3 _____

4 _____

5 _____

5 things i want to do in my life

1 _____

2 _____

3 _____

4 _____

5 _____

today's mantra

_____

this made me smile today:

_____

what i'm looking forward to tomorrow:

_____

—— | —— | ——

i am grateful for:

_____

_____

_____

_____

_____

5 things i need to do today   *5 things i want to do in my life*

1 _____   1 _____

2 _____   2 _____

3 _____   3 _____

4 _____   4 _____

5 _____   5 _____

today's mantra

_____

this made me smile today:

_____

what i'm looking forward to tomorrow:

_____

—— | —— | ——

i am grateful for:

_____

_____

_____

_____

_____

_____

5 things i need to do today   *5 things i want to do in my life*

1 _____   1 _____

2 _____   2 _____

3 _____   3 _____

4 _____   4 _____

5 _____   5 _____

today's mantra

_____

this made me smile today:

_____

what i'm looking forward to tomorrow:

_____

date

___ | ___ | ___

i am grateful for:

_____

_____

_____

_____

_____

_____

5 things i need to do today

1 _____

2 _____

3 _____

4 _____

5 _____

5 things i want to do in my life

1 _____

2 _____

3 _____

4 _____

5 _____

today's mantra

_____

this made me smile today:

_____

what i'm looking forward to tomorrow:

_____

i am grateful for:

_____

_____

_____

_____

_____

_____

5 things i need to do today

1 _____

2 _____

3 _____

4 _____

5 _____

5 things i want to do in my life

1 _____

2 _____

3 _____

4 _____

5 _____

today's mantra

_____

this made me smile today:

_____

what i'm looking forward to tomorrow:

_____

date

___ | ___ | ___

i am grateful for:

_____

_____

_____

_____

_____

_____

5 things i need to do today

1 _____

2 _____

3 _____

4 _____

5 _____

5 things i want to do in my life

1 _____

2 _____

3 _____

4 _____

5 _____

today's mantra

_____

this made me smile today:

_____

what i'm looking forward to tomorrow:

_____

i am grateful for:

_____

_____

_____

_____

_____

_____

5 things i need to do today

1 _____

2 _____

3 _____

4 _____

5 _____

5 things i want to do in my life

1 _____

2 _____

3 _____

4 _____

5 _____

today's mantra

_____

this made me smile today:

_____

what i'm looking forward to tomorrow:

_____

date

—— | —— | ——

i am grateful for:

_____

_____

_____

_____

_____

_____

_____

5 things i need to do today   *5 things i want to do in my life*

1 _____   1 _____

2 _____   2 _____

3 _____   3 _____

4 _____   4 _____

5 _____   5 _____

today's mantra

_____

this made me smile today:

_____

what i'm looking forward to tomorrow:

_____

—— | —— | ——

i am grateful for:

_____

_____

_____

_____

_____

_____

5 things i need to do today

1 _____

2 _____

3 _____

4 _____

5 _____

5 things i want to do in my life

1 _____

2 _____

3 _____

4 _____

5 _____

today's mantra

_____

this made me smile today:

_____

what i'm looking forward to tomorrow:

_____

date

— | — | —

i am grateful for:

_____

_____

_____

_____

_____

_____

5 things i need to do today   *5 things i want to do in my life*

1 _____   1 _____

2 _____   2 _____

3 _____   3 _____

4 _____   4 _____

5 _____   5 _____

today's mantra

_____

this made me smile today:

_____

what i'm looking forward to tomorrow:

_____

be patient with yourself

you are the magic of the Universe

unfolding at its own rhythm

—— | —— | ——

i am grateful for:

_____

_____

_____

_____

_____

_____

5 things i need to do today   *5 things i want to do in my life*

1 _____   1 _____

2 _____   2 _____

3 _____   3 _____

4 _____   4 _____

5 _____   5 _____

today's mantra

_____

this made me smile today:

_____

what i'm looking forward to tomorrow:

_____

date

___ | ___ | ___

i am grateful for:

_____

_____

_____

_____

_____

_____

5 things i need to do today   *5 things i want to do in my life*

1 _____   1 _____

2 _____   2 _____

3 _____   3 _____

4 _____   4 _____

5 _____   5 _____

today's mantra

_____

this made me smile today:

_____

what i'm looking forward to tomorrow:

_____

date

___ | ___ | ___

i am grateful for:

_____

_____

_____

_____

_____

_____

5 things i need to do today

1 _____

2 _____

3 _____

4 _____

5 _____

5 things i want to do in my life

1 _____

2 _____

3 _____

4 _____

5 _____

today's mantra

_____

this made me smile today:

_____

what i'm looking forward to tomorrow:

_____

date

—— | —— | ——

i am grateful for:

_____

_____

_____

_____

_____

_____

5 things i need to do today   *5 things i want to do in my life*

1 _____   1 _____

2 _____   2 _____

3 _____   3 _____

4 _____   4 _____

5 _____   5 _____

today's mantra

_____

this made me smile today:

_____

what i'm looking forward to tomorrow:

_____

___ | ___ | ___

i am grateful for:

_____

_____

_____

_____

_____

_____

5 things i need to do today	*5 things i want to do in my life*
1 _____	1 _____
2 _____	2 _____
3 _____	3 _____
4 _____	4 _____
5 _____	5 _____

today's mantra

_____

this made me smile today:

_____

what i'm looking forward to tomorrow:

_____

date

—— | —— | ——

i am grateful for:

_____

_____

_____

_____

_____

5 things i need to do today   *5 things i want to do in my life*

1 _____   1 _____

2 _____   2 _____

3 _____   3 _____

4 _____   4 _____

5 _____   5 _____

today's mantra

_____

this made me smile today:

_____

what i'm looking forward to tomorrow:

_____

date

___ | ___ | ___

i am grateful for:

_____

_____

_____

_____

_____

_____

5 things i need to do today

1 _____

2 _____

3 _____

4 _____

5 _____

5 things i want to do in my life

1 _____

2 _____

3 _____

4 _____

5 _____

today's mantra

_____

this made me smile today:

_____

what i'm looking forward to tomorrow:

_____

date

—— | —— | ——

i am grateful for:

_____

_____

_____

_____

_____

5 things i need to do today	*5 things i want to do in my life*
1 _____	1 _____
2 _____	2 _____
3 _____	3 _____
4 _____	4 _____
5 _____	5 _____

today's mantra

_____

this made me smile today:

_____

what i'm looking forward to tomorrow:

_____

95

___ | ___ | ___

i am grateful for:

_____

_____

_____

_____

_____

_____

5 things i need to do today

1 _____

2 _____

3 _____

4 _____

5 _____

5 things i want to do in my life

1 _____

2 _____

3 _____

4 _____

5 _____

today's mantra

_____

this made me smile today:

_____

what i'm looking forward to tomorrow:

_____

date

___ | ___ | ___

i am grateful for:

_____

_____

_____

_____

_____

_____

5 things i need to do today   *5 things i want to do in my life*

1 _____   1 _____

2 _____   2 _____

3 _____   3 _____

4 _____   4 _____

5 _____   5 _____

today's mantra

_____

this made me smile today:

_____

what i'm looking forward to tomorrow:

_____

date

—— | —— | ——

i am grateful for:

_____

_____

_____

_____

_____

_____

5 things i need to do today	*5 things i want to do in my life*
1	1
2	2
3	3
4	4
5	5

today's mantra

_____

this made me smile today:

_____

what i'm looking forward to tomorrow:

_____

date

—— | —— | ——

i am grateful for:

_____

_____

_____

_____

_____

_____

5 things i need to do today   *5 things i want to do in my life*

1 _____   1 _____

2 _____   2 _____

3 _____   3 _____

4 _____   4 _____

5 _____   5 _____

today's mantra

_____

this made me smile today:

_____

what i'm looking forward to tomorrow:

_____

date

—— | —— | ——

i am grateful for:

_____

_____

_____

_____

_____

_____

5 things i need to do today

1 _____

2 _____

3 _____

4 _____

5 _____

5 things i want to do in my life

1 _____

2 _____

3 _____

4 _____

5 _____

today's mantra

_____

this made me smile today:

_____

what i'm looking forward to tomorrow:

_____

date

___ | ___ | ___

i am grateful for:

_____

_____

_____

_____

_____

_____

5 things i need to do today

1 _____

2 _____

3 _____

4 _____

5 _____

5 things i want to do in my life

1 _____

2 _____

3 _____

4 _____

5 _____

today's mantra

_____

this made me smile today:

_____

what i'm looking forward to tomorrow:

_____

date

—— | —— | ——

i am grateful for:

_____

_____

_____

_____

_____

5 things i need to do today

1 _____

2 _____

3 _____

4 _____

5 _____

5 things i want to do in my life

1 _____

2 _____

3 _____

4 _____

5 _____

today's mantra

_____

this made me smile today:

_____

what i'm looking forward to tomorrow:

_____

date

___ | ___ | ___

i am grateful for:

_____

_____

_____

_____

_____

_____

5 things i need to do today

1 _____

2 _____

3 _____

4 _____

5 _____

5 things i want to do in my life

1 _____

2 _____

3 _____

4 _____

5 _____

today's mantra

_____

this made me smile today:

_____

what i'm looking forward to tomorrow:

_____

date

___ | ___ | ___

i am grateful for:

_____

_____

_____

_____

_____

_____

5 things i need to do today

1 _____

2 _____

3 _____

4 _____

5 _____

5 things i want to do in my life

1 _____

2 _____

3 _____

4 _____

5 _____

today's mantra

_____

this made me smile today:

_____

what i'm looking forward to tomorrow:

_____

date

___ | ___ | ___

i am grateful for:

_____

_____

_____

_____

_____

5 things i need to do today

1 _____

2 _____

3 _____

4 _____

5 _____

5 things i want to do in my life

1 _____

2 _____

3 _____

4 _____

5 _____

today's mantra

_____

this made me smile today:

_____

what i'm looking forward to tomorrow:

_____

date

___ | ___ | ___

i am grateful for:

_____

_____

_____

_____

_____

_____

5 things i need to do today

1 _____

2 _____

3 _____

4 _____

5 _____

5 things i want to do in my life

1 _____

2 _____

3 _____

4 _____

5 _____

today's mantra

_____

this made me smile today:

_____

what i'm looking forward to tomorrow:

_____

date

___ | ___ | ___

i am grateful for:

_____

_____

_____

_____

_____

_____

5 things i need to do today   *5 things i want to do in my life*

1 _____   1 _____

2 _____   2 _____

3 _____   3 _____

4 _____   4 _____

5 _____   5 _____

today's mantra

_____

this made me smile today:

_____

what i'm looking forward to tomorrow:

_____

it always works out,

it's just a question of how.

date

—— | —— | ——

i am grateful for:

_____

_____

_____

_____

_____

_____

5 things i need to do today	*5 things i want to do in my life*
1 _____	1 _____
2 _____	2 _____
3 _____	3 _____
4 _____	4 _____
5 _____	5 _____

today's mantra

_____

this made me smile today:

_____

what i'm looking forward to tomorrow:

_____

date

___ | ___ | ___

i am grateful for:

_____

_____

_____

_____

_____

_____

5 things i need to do today   *5 things i want to do in my life*

1 _____   1 _____

2 _____   2 _____

3 _____   3 _____

4 _____   4 _____

5 _____   5 _____

today's mantra

_____

this made me smile today:

_____

what i'm looking forward to tomorrow:

_____

i am grateful for:

_____

_____

_____

_____

_____

_____

5 things i need to do today

1 _____

2 _____

3 _____

4 _____

5 _____

5 things i want to do in my life

1 _____

2 _____

3 _____

4 _____

5 _____

today's mantra

_____

this made me smile today:

_____

what i'm looking forward to tomorrow:

_____

date

___ | ___ | ___

i am grateful for:

_____

_____

_____

_____

_____

_____

5 things i need to do today

1 _____

2 _____

3 _____

4 _____

5 _____

5 things i want to do in my life

1 _____

2 _____

3 _____

4 _____

5 _____

today's mantra

_____

this made me smile today:

_____

what i'm looking forward to tomorrow:

_____

i am grateful for:

_____

_____

_____

_____

_____

_____

5 things i need to do today

1 _____

2 _____

3 _____

4 _____

5 _____

5 things i want to do in my life

1 _____

2 _____

3 _____

4 _____

5 _____

today's mantra

_____

this made me smile today:

_____

what i'm looking forward to tomorrow:

_____

date

___ | ___ | ___

i am grateful for:

_____

_____

_____

_____

_____

_____

5 things i need to do today

1 _____

2 _____

3 _____

4 _____

5 _____

5 things i want to do in my life

1 _____

2 _____

3 _____

4 _____

5 _____

today's mantra

_____

this made me smile today:

_____

what i'm looking forward to tomorrow:

_____

date

___ | ___ | ___

i am grateful for:

_____

_____

_____

_____

_____

5 things i need to do today

1 _____

2 _____

3 _____

4 _____

5 _____

5 things i want to do in my life

1 _____

2 _____

3 _____

4 _____

5 _____

today's mantra

_____

this made me smile today:

_____

what i'm looking forward to tomorrow:

_____

date

___ | ___ | ___

i am grateful for:

_____

_____

_____

_____

_____

5 things i need to do today   *5 things i want to do in my life*

1 _____   1 _____

2 _____   2 _____

3 _____   3 _____

4 _____   4 _____

5 _____   5 _____

today's mantra

_____

this made me smile today:

_____

what i'm looking forward to tomorrow:

_____

date

___ | ___ | ___

i am grateful for:

_____

_____

_____

_____

_____

_____

5 things i need to do today

1 _____

2 _____

3 _____

4 _____

5 _____

5 things i want to do in my life

1 _____

2 _____

3 _____

4 _____

5 _____

today's mantra

_____

this made me smile today:

_____

what i'm looking forward to tomorrow:

_____

date

—— | —— | ——

i am grateful for:

_____

_____

_____

_____

_____

_____

5 things i need to do today

1 _____

2 _____

3 _____

4 _____

5 _____

5 things i want to do in my life

1 _____

2 _____

3 _____

4 _____

5 _____

today's mantra

_____

this made me smile today:

_____

what i'm looking forward to tomorrow:

_____

date

___ | ___ | ___

i am grateful for:

_____

_____

_____

_____

_____

_____

5 things i need to do today

1 _____

2 _____

3 _____

4 _____

5 _____

5 things i want to do in my life

1 _____

2 _____

3 _____

4 _____

5 _____

today's mantra

_____

this made me smile today:

_____

what i'm looking forward to tomorrow:

_____

date

___ | ___ | ___

i am grateful for:

_____

_____

_____

_____

_____

_____

5 things i need to do today　　　　*5 things i want to do in my life*

1 _____　　　1 _____

2 _____　　　2 _____

3 _____　　　3 _____

4 _____　　　4 _____

5 _____　　　5 _____

today's mantra

_____

this made me smile today:

_____

what i'm looking forward to tomorrow:

_____

—— | —— | ——

i am grateful for:

_____

_____

_____

_____

_____

5 things i need to do today

1 _____

2 _____

3 _____

4 _____

5 _____

5 things i want to do in my life

1 _____

2 _____

3 _____

4 _____

5 _____

today's mantra

_____

this made me smile today:

_____

what i'm looking forward to tomorrow:

_____

date

___ | ___ | ___

i am grateful for:

_____

_____

_____

_____

_____

5 things i need to do today

1 _____

2 _____

3 _____

4 _____

5 _____

5 things i want to do in my life

1 _____

2 _____

3 _____

4 _____

5 _____

today's mantra

_____

this made me smile today:

_____

what i'm looking forward to tomorrow:

_____

date

___ | ___ | ___

i am grateful for:

_____

_____

_____

_____

_____

_____

5 things i need to do today

1 _____

2 _____

3 _____

4 _____

5 _____

5 things i want to do in my life

1 _____

2 _____

3 _____

4 _____

5 _____

today's mantra

_____

this made me smile today:

_____

what i'm looking forward to tomorrow:

_____

date

___ | ___ | ___

i am grateful for:

_____

_____

_____

_____

_____

5 things i need to do today

1 _____

2 _____

3 _____

4 _____

5 _____

5 things i want to do in my life

1 _____

2 _____

3 _____

4 _____

5 _____

today's mantra

_____

this made me smile today:

_____

what i'm looking forward to tomorrow:

_____

date

___ | ___ | ___

i am grateful for:

_____

_____

_____

_____

_____

_____

5 things i need to do today

1 _____

2 _____

3 _____

4 _____

5 _____

5 things i want to do in my life

1 _____

2 _____

3 _____

4 _____

5 _____

today's mantra

_____

this made me smile today:

_____

what i'm looking forward to tomorrow:

_____

date

— | — | —

i am grateful for:

_____

_____

_____

_____

_____

_____

5 things i need to do today

1 _____

2 _____

3 _____

4 _____

5 _____

5 things i want to do in my life

1 _____

2 _____

3 _____

4 _____

5 _____

today's mantra

_____

this made me smile today:

_____

what i'm looking forward to tomorrow:

_____

date

___ | ___ | ___

i am grateful for:

_____

_____

_____

_____

_____

_____

5 things i need to do today

1 _____
2 _____
3 _____
4 _____
5 _____

5 things i want to do in my life

1 _____
2 _____
3 _____
4 _____
5 _____

today's mantra

_____

this made me smile today:

_____

what i'm looking forward to tomorrow:

_____

date

—— | —— | ——

i am grateful for:

_____

_____

_____

_____

_____

_____

5 things i need to do today	*5 things i want to do in my life*
1 _____	1 _____
2 _____	2 _____
3 _____	3 _____
4 _____	4 _____
5 _____	5 _____

today's mantra

_____

this made me smile today:

_____

what i'm looking forward to tomorrow:

_____

once she became
comfortable with
being uncomfortable,
she was free to grow.

date

—— | —— | ——

i am grateful for:

_____

_____

_____

_____

_____

☀

5 things i need to do today	*5 things i want to do in my life*
1 _____	1 _____
2 _____	2 _____
3 _____	3 _____
4 _____	4 _____
5 _____	5 _____

today's mantra

_____

☽

this made me smile today:

_____

what i'm looking forward to tomorrow:

_____

date

___ | ___ | ___

i am grateful for:

_____

_____

_____

_____

_____

_____

5 things i need to do today

1 _____

2 _____

3 _____

4 _____

5 _____

5 things i want to do in my life

1 _____

2 _____

3 _____

4 _____

5 _____

today's mantra

_____

this made me smile today:

_____

what i'm looking forward to tomorrow:

_____

date

___ | ___ | ___

i am grateful for:

_____

_____

_____

_____

_____

_____

5 things i need to do today	*5 things i want to do in my life*
1 _____	1 _____
2 _____	2 _____
3 _____	3 _____
4 _____	4 _____
5 _____	5 _____

today's mantra

_____

this made me smile today:

_____

what i'm looking forward to tomorrow:

_____

date

—— | —— | ——

i am grateful for:

_____

_____

_____

_____

_____

_____

5 things i need to do today

1 _____

2 _____

3 _____

4 _____

5 _____

5 things i want to do in my life

1 _____

2 _____

3 _____

4 _____

5 _____

today's mantra

_____

this made me smile today:

_____

what i'm looking forward to tomorrow:

_____

i am grateful for:

_____

_____

_____

_____

_____

_____

5 things i need to do today   *5 things i want to do in my life*

1 _____   1 _____

2 _____   2 _____

3 _____   3 _____

4 _____   4 _____

5 _____   5 _____

today's mantra

_____

this made me smile today:

_____

what i'm looking forward to tomorrow:

_____

date

—— | —— | ——

i am grateful for:

_____

_____

_____

_____

_____

_____

5 things i need to do today   *5 things i want to do in my life*

1 _____   1 _____

2 _____   2 _____

3 _____   3 _____

4 _____   4 _____

5 _____   5 _____

today's mantra

_____

this made me smile today:

_____

what i'm looking forward to tomorrow:

_____

date

___ | ___ | ___

i am grateful for:

_____

_____

_____

_____

_____

_____

5 things i need to do today

1 _____

2 _____

3 _____

4 _____

5 _____

5 things i want to do in my life

1 _____

2 _____

3 _____

4 _____

5 _____

today's mantra

_____

this made me smile today:

_____

what i'm looking forward to tomorrow:

_____

date

—— | —— | ——

i am grateful for:

_____

_____

_____

_____

_____

_____

5 things i need to do today   *5 things i want to do in my life*

1 _____   1 _____

2 _____   2 _____

3 _____   3 _____

4 _____   4 _____

5 _____   5 _____

today's mantra

_____

this made me smile today:

_____

what i'm looking forward to tomorrow:

_____

date

___ | ___ | ___

i am grateful for:

_____

_____

_____

_____

_____

_____

5 things i need to do today

1 _____
2 _____
3 _____
4 _____
5 _____

5 things i want to do in my life

1 _____
2 _____
3 _____
4 _____
5 _____

today's mantra

_____

this made me smile today:

_____

what i'm looking forward to tomorrow:

_____

date

— | — | —

i am grateful for:

_____

_____

_____

_____

_____

5 things i need to do today

1 _____

2 _____

3 _____

4 _____

5 _____

5 things i want to do in my life

1 _____

2 _____

3 _____

4 _____

5 _____

today's mantra

_____

this made me smile today:

_____

what i'm looking forward to tomorrow:

_____

date

___ | ___ | ___

i am grateful for:

_____

_____

_____

_____

_____

_____

5 things i need to do today

1 _____

2 _____

3 _____

4 _____

5 _____

5 things i want to do in my life

1 _____

2 _____

3 _____

4 _____

5 _____

today's mantra

_____

this made me smile today:

_____

what i'm looking forward to tomorrow:

_____

date

___ | ___ | ___

i am grateful for:

_____

_____

_____

_____

_____

_____

5 things i need to do today   *5 things i want to do in my life*

1 _____   1 _____

2 _____   2 _____

3 _____   3 _____

4 _____   4 _____

5 _____   5 _____

today's mantra

_____

this made me smile today:

_____

what i'm looking forward to tomorrow:

_____

i am grateful for:

_____

_____

_____

_____

_____

_____

5 things i need to do today

1 _____

2 _____

3 _____

4 _____

5 _____

5 things i want to do in my life

1 _____

2 _____

3 _____

4 _____

5 _____

today's mantra

_____

this made me smile today:

_____

what i'm looking forward to tomorrow:

_____

date

—— | —— | ——

i am grateful for:

_____

_____

_____

_____

_____

_____

5 things i need to do today	*5 things i want to do in my life*
1 _____	1 _____
2 _____	2 _____
3 _____	3 _____
4 _____	4 _____
5 _____	5 _____

today's mantra

_____

this made me smile today:

_____

what i'm looking forward to tomorrow:

_____

145

—— | —— | ——

i am grateful for:

_____

_____

_____

_____

_____

5 things i need to do today

1 _____

2 _____

3 _____

4 _____

5 _____

5 things i want to do in my life

1 _____

2 _____

3 _____

4 _____

5 _____

today's mantra

_____

this made me smile today:

_____

what i'm looking forward to tomorrow:

_____

date

—— | —— | ——

i am grateful for:

_____

_____

_____

_____

_____

_____

5 things i need to do today

1 _____

2 _____

3 _____

4 _____

5 _____

5 things i want to do in my life

1 _____

2 _____

3 _____

4 _____

5 _____

today's mantra

_____

this made me smile today:

_____

what i'm looking forward to tomorrow:

_____

date

___ | ___ | ___

i am grateful for:

_____

_____

_____

_____

_____

_____

5 things i need to do today

1 _____

2 _____

3 _____

4 _____

5 _____

5 things i want to do in my life

1 _____

2 _____

3 _____

4 _____

5 _____

today's mantra

_____

this made me smile today:

_____

what i'm looking forward to tomorrow:

_____

date

___ | ___ | ___

i am grateful for:

_____

_____

_____

_____

_____

_____

5 things i need to do today

1 _____

2 _____

3 _____

4 _____

5 _____

5 things i want to do in my life

1 _____

2 _____

3 _____

4 _____

5 _____

today's mantra

_____

this made me smile today:

_____

what i'm looking forward to tomorrow:

_____

date

—— | —— | ——

i am grateful for:

_____

_____

_____

_____

_____

_____

5 things i need to do today

1 _____

2 _____

3 _____

4 _____

5 _____

5 things i want to do in my life

1 _____

2 _____

3 _____

4 _____

5 _____

today's mantra

_____

this made me smile today:

_____

what i'm looking forward to tomorrow:

_____

date

— | — | —

i am grateful for:

_____

_____

_____

_____

_____

_____

5 things i need to do today

1 _____
2 _____
3 _____
4 _____
5 _____

5 things i want to do in my life

1 _____
2 _____
3 _____
4 _____
5 _____

today's mantra

_____

this made me smile today:

_____

what i'm looking forward to tomorrow:

_____

growth isn't linear
there is no direct line from

A   to   B

the path is full of twists and turns

it makes you think you're heading
backward

when really you're moving
forward

it takes time, dedication, and patience.
it doesn't always make sense,
but neither does magic.

i am grateful for:

_____

_____

_____

_____

_____

_____

5 things i need to do today

1 _____

2 _____

3 _____

4 _____

5 _____

5 things i want to do in my life

1 _____

2 _____

3 _____

4 _____

5 _____

today's mantra

_____

this made me smile today:

_____

what i'm looking forward to tomorrow:

_____

date

___ | ___ | ___

i am grateful for:

_____

_____

_____

_____

_____

_____

5 things i need to do today

1 _____

2 _____

3 _____

4 _____

5 _____

5 things i want to do in my life

1 _____

2 _____

3 _____

4 _____

5 _____

today's mantra

_____

this made me smile today:

_____

what i'm looking forward to tomorrow:

_____

date

—— | —— | ——

i am grateful for:

_____

_____

_____

_____

_____

_____

5 things i need to do today	*5 things i want to do in my life*
1 _____	1 _____
2 _____	2 _____
3 _____	3 _____
4 _____	4 _____
5 _____	5 _____

today's mantra

_____

this made me smile today:

_____

what i'm looking forward to tomorrow:

_____

date

___ | ___ | ___

i am grateful for:

_____

_____

_____

_____

_____

_____

5 things i need to do today

1 _____

2 _____

3 _____

4 _____

5 _____

5 things i want to do in my life

1 _____

2 _____

3 _____

4 _____

5 _____

today's mantra

_____

this made me smile today:

_____

what i'm looking forward to tomorrow:

_____

—— | —— | ——

i am grateful for:

_____

_____

_____

_____

_____

_____

5 things i need to do today

1 _____

2 _____

3 _____

4 _____

5 _____

5 things i want to do in my life

1 _____

2 _____

3 _____

4 _____

5 _____

today's mantra

_____

this made me smile today:

_____

what i'm looking forward to tomorrow:

_____

date

___ | ___ | ___

i am grateful for:

_____

_____

_____

_____

_____

_____

5 things i need to do today   *5 things i want to do in my life*

1 _____   1 _____

2 _____   2 _____

3 _____   3 _____

4 _____   4 _____

5 _____   5 _____

today's mantra

_____

this made me smile today:

_____

what i'm looking forward to tomorrow:

_____

i am grateful for:

_____

_____

_____

_____

_____

_____

5 things i need to do today

1 _____

2 _____

3 _____

4 _____

5 _____

5 things i want to do in my life

1 _____

2 _____

3 _____

4 _____

5 _____

today's mantra

_____

this made me smile today:

_____

what i'm looking forward to tomorrow:

_____

date

___ | ___ | ___

i am grateful for:

_____

_____

_____

_____

_____

_____

5 things i need to do today   *5 things i want to do in my life*

1 _____   1 _____

2 _____   2 _____

3 _____   3 _____

4 _____   4 _____

5 _____   5 _____

today's mantra

_____

this made me smile today:

_____

what i'm looking forward to tomorrow:

_____

i am grateful for:

_____

_____

_____

_____

_____

_____

5 things i need to do today

1 _____

2 _____

3 _____

4 _____

5 _____

5 things i want to do in my life

1 _____

2 _____

3 _____

4 _____

5 _____

today's mantra

_____

this made me smile today:

_____

what i'm looking forward to tomorrow:

_____

date

___ | ___ | ___

i am grateful for:

_____

_____

_____

_____

_____

_____

5 things i need to do today

1 _____

2 _____

3 _____

4 _____

5 _____

5 things i want to do in my life

1 _____

2 _____

3 _____

4 _____

5 _____

today's mantra

_____

this made me smile today:

_____

what i'm looking forward to tomorrow:

_____

date

—— | —— | ——

i am grateful for:

_____

_____

_____

_____

_____

5 things i need to do today

1 _____

2 _____

3 _____

4 _____

5 _____

5 things i want to do in my life

1 _____

2 _____

3 _____

4 _____

5 _____

today's mantra

_____

this made me smile today:

_____

what i'm looking forward to tomorrow:

_____

date

___ | ___ | ___

i am grateful for:

_____

_____

_____

_____

_____

_____

5 things i need to do today

1 _____

2 _____

3 _____

4 _____

5 _____

5 things i want to do in my life

1 _____

2 _____

3 _____

4 _____

5 _____

today's mantra

_____

this made me smile today:

_____

what i'm looking forward to tomorrow:

_____

___ | ___ | ___

i am grateful for:

_____

_____

_____

_____

_____

_____

5 things i need to do today   *5 things i want to do in my life*

1 _____   1 _____

2 _____   2 _____

3 _____   3 _____

4 _____   4 _____

5 _____   5 _____

today's mantra

_____

this made me smile today:

_____

what i'm looking forward to tomorrow:

_____

date

___ | ___ | ___

i am grateful for:

_____

_____

_____

_____

_____

_____

5 things i need to do today

1 _____

2 _____

3 _____

4 _____

5 _____

5 things i want to do in my life

1 _____

2 _____

3 _____

4 _____

5 _____

today's mantra

_____

this made me smile today:

_____

what i'm looking forward to tomorrow:

_____

date

___ | ___ | ___

i am grateful for:

_____

_____

_____

_____

_____

_____

5 things i need to do today   *5 things i want to do in my life*

1 _____   1 _____

2 _____   2 _____

3 _____   3 _____

4 _____   4 _____

5 _____   5 _____

today's mantra

_____

this made me smile today:

_____

what i'm looking forward to tomorrow:

_____

—— | —— | ——

i am grateful for:

_____

_____

_____

_____

_____

_____

5 things i need to do today   *5 things i want to do in my life*

1 _____   1 _____

2 _____   2 _____

3 _____   3 _____

4 _____   4 _____

5 _____   5 _____

today's mantra

_____

this made me smile today:

_____

what i'm looking forward to tomorrow:

_____

date

___ | ___ | ___

i am grateful for:

_____

_____

_____

_____

_____

_____

5 things i need to do today

1 _____

2 _____

3 _____

4 _____

5 _____

5 things i want to do in my life

1 _____

2 _____

3 _____

4 _____

5 _____

today's mantra

_____

this made me smile today:

_____

what i'm looking forward to tomorrow:

_____

170

date

—— | —— | ——

i am grateful for:

_____

_____

_____

_____

_____

_____

5 things i need to do today

1 _____

2 _____

3 _____

4 _____

5 _____

5 things i want to do in my life

1 _____

2 _____

3 _____

4 _____

5 _____

today's mantra

_____

this made me smile today:

_____

what i'm looking forward to tomorrow:

_____

—— | —— | ——

i am grateful for:

_____

_____

_____

_____

_____

_____

5 things i need to do today

1 _____

2 _____

3 _____

4 _____

5 _____

5 things i want to do in my life

1 _____

2 _____

3 _____

4 _____

5 _____

today's mantra

_____

this made me smile today:

_____

what i'm looking forward to tomorrow:

_____

date

— | — | —

i am grateful for:

_____

_____

_____

_____

_____

_____

5 things i need to do today

1 _____

2 _____

3 _____

4 _____

5 _____

5 things i want to do in my life

1 _____

2 _____

3 _____

4 _____

5 _____

today's mantra

_____

this made me smile today:

_____

what i'm looking forward to tomorrow:

_____

☾

like the Moon, your magic

will come when you least expect it.

i am grateful for:

_____

_____

_____

_____

_____

_____

5 things i need to do today

1 _____

2 _____

3 _____

4 _____

5 _____

5 things i want to do in my life

1 _____

2 _____

3 _____

4 _____

5 _____

today's mantra

_____

this made me smile today:

_____

what i'm looking forward to tomorrow:

_____

date

___ | ___ | ___

i am grateful for:

_____

_____

_____

_____

_____

_____

5 things i need to do today   *5 things i want to do in my life*

1 _____   1 _____

2 _____   2 _____

3 _____   3 _____

4 _____   4 _____

5 _____   5 _____

today's mantra

_____

this made me smile today:

_____

what i'm looking forward to tomorrow:

_____

i am grateful for:

_____

_____

_____

_____

_____

5 things i need to do today

1 _____

2 _____

3 _____

4 _____

5 _____

5 things i want to do in my life

1 _____

2 _____

3 _____

4 _____

5 _____

today's mantra

_____

this made me smile today:

_____

what i'm looking forward to tomorrow:

_____

date

___ | ___ | ___

i am grateful for:

_____

_____

_____

_____

_____

_____

5 things i need to do today   *5 things i want to do in my life*

1 _____   1 _____

2 _____   2 _____

3 _____   3 _____

4 _____   4 _____

5 _____   5 _____

today's mantra

_____

this made me smile today:

_____

what i'm looking forward to tomorrow:

_____

— | — | —

i am grateful for:

_____

_____

_____

_____

_____

_____

5 things i need to do today

1 _____

2 _____

3 _____

4 _____

5 _____

5 things i want to do in my life

1 _____

2 _____

3 _____

4 _____

5 _____

today's mantra

_____

this made me smile today:

_____

what i'm looking forward to tomorrow:

_____

date

___ | ___ | ___

i am grateful for:

_____

_____

_____

_____

_____

_____

5 things i need to do today

1 _____

2 _____

3 _____

4 _____

5 _____

5 things i want to do in my life

1 _____

2 _____

3 _____

4 _____

5 _____

today's mantra

_____

this made me smile today:

_____

what i'm looking forward to tomorrow:

_____

date

___ | ___ | ___

i am grateful for:

_____

_____

_____

_____

_____

5 things i need to do today

1 _____

2 _____

3 _____

4 _____

5 _____

5 things i want to do in my life

1 _____

2 _____

3 _____

4 _____

5 _____

today's mantra

_____

this made me smile today:

_____

what i'm looking forward to tomorrow:

_____

date

—— | —— | ——

i am grateful for:

_____

_____

_____

_____

_____

_____

5 things i need to do today

1 _____

2 _____

3 _____

4 _____

5 _____

5 things i want to do in my life

1 _____

2 _____

3 _____

4 _____

5 _____

today's mantra

_____

this made me smile today:

_____

what i'm looking forward to tomorrow:

_____

i am grateful for:

_____

_____

_____

_____

_____

_____

5 things i need to do today

1 _____

2 _____

3 _____

4 _____

5 _____

5 things i want to do in my life

1 _____

2 _____

3 _____

4 _____

5 _____

today's mantra

_____

this made me smile today:

_____

what i'm looking forward to tomorrow:

_____

date

___ | ___ | ___

i am grateful for:

---

5 things i need to do today

1 ___
2 ___
3 ___
4 ___
5 ___

5 things i want to do in my life

1 ___
2 ___
3 ___
4 ___
5 ___

today's mantra

---

this made me smile today:

---

what i'm looking forward to tomorrow:

___ | ___ | ___

i am grateful for:

_____

_____

_____

_____

_____

5 things i need to do today

1 _____

2 _____

3 _____

4 _____

5 _____

5 things i want to do in my life

1 _____

2 _____

3 _____

4 _____

5 _____

today's mantra

_____

this made me smile today:

_____

what i'm looking forward to tomorrow:

_____

date

___ | ___ | ___

i am grateful for:

_____
_____
_____
_____
_____
_____

5 things i need to do today	*5 things i want to do in my life*
1 _____	1 _____
2 _____	2 _____
3 _____	3 _____
4 _____	4 _____
5 _____	5 _____

today's mantra

_____

this made me smile today:

_____

what i'm looking forward to tomorrow:

_____

date

___ | ___ | ___

i am grateful for:

_____

_____

_____

_____

_____

_____

5 things i need to do today

1 _____

2 _____

3 _____

4 _____

5 _____

5 things i want to do in my life

1 _____

2 _____

3 _____

4 _____

5 _____

today's mantra

_____

this made me smile today:

_____

what i'm looking forward to tomorrow:

_____

date

—— | —— | ——

i am grateful for:

_____

_____

_____

_____

_____

_____

5 things i need to do today

1 _____

2 _____

3 _____

4 _____

5 _____

5 things i want to do in my life

1 _____

2 _____

3 _____

4 _____

5 _____

today's mantra

_____

this made me smile today:

_____

what i'm looking forward to tomorrow:

_____

—— | —— | ——

i am grateful for:

_____

_____

_____

_____

_____

_____

5 things i need to do today

1 _____

2 _____

3 _____

4 _____

5 _____

5 things i want to do in my life

1 _____

2 _____

3 _____

4 _____

5 _____

today's mantra

_____

this made me smile today:

_____

what i'm looking forward to tomorrow:

_____

i am grateful for:

_____

_____

_____

_____

_____

_____

5 things i need to do today

1 _____

2 _____

3 _____

4 _____

5 _____

5 things i want to do in my life

1 _____

2 _____

3 _____

4 _____

5 _____

today's mantra

_____

this made me smile today:

_____

what i'm looking forward to tomorrow:

_____

i am grateful for:

_____

_____

_____

_____

_____

_____

5 things i need to do today

1 _____

2 _____

3 _____

4 _____

5 _____

5 things i want to do in my life

1 _____

2 _____

3 _____

4 _____

5 _____

today's mantra

_____

this made me smile today:

_____

what i'm looking forward to tomorrow:

_____

date

—— | —— | ——

i am grateful for:

_____

_____

_____

_____

_____

5 things i need to do today   *5 things i want to do in my life*

1 _____   1 _____

2 _____   2 _____

3 _____   3 _____

4 _____   4 _____

5 _____   5 _____

today's mantra

_____

this made me smile today:

_____

what i'm looking forward to tomorrow:

_____

i am grateful for:

_____

_____

_____

_____

_____

_____

5 things i need to do today

1 _____

2 _____

3 _____

4 _____

5 _____

5 things i want to do in my life

1 _____

2 _____

3 _____

4 _____

5 _____

today's mantra

_____

this made me smile today:

_____

what i'm looking forward to tomorrow:

_____

date

—— | —— | ——

i am grateful for:

_____

_____

_____

_____

_____

_____

5 things i need to do today

1 _____

2 _____

3 _____

4 _____

5 _____

5 things i want to do in my life

1 _____

2 _____

3 _____

4 _____

5 _____

today's mantra

_____

this made me smile today:

_____

what i'm looking forward to tomorrow:

_____

just because it's not working out,

doesn't mean it's not working out.

date

—— | —— | ——

i am grateful for:

_____

_____

_____

_____

_____

_____

5 things i need to do today	*5 things i want to do in my life*
1 _____	1 _____
2 _____	2 _____
3 _____	3 _____
4 _____	4 _____
5 _____	5 _____

today's mantra

_____

this made me smile today:

_____

what i'm looking forward to tomorrow:

_____

date

—— | —— | ——

i am grateful for:

_____

_____

_____

_____

_____

5 things i need to do today   *5 things i want to do in my life*

1 _____   1 _____

2 _____   2 _____

3 _____   3 _____

4 _____   4 _____

5 _____   5 _____

today's mantra

_____

this made me smile today:

_____

what i'm looking forward to tomorrow:

_____

date

___ | ___ | ___

i am grateful for:

_____

_____

_____

_____

_____

_____

5 things i need to do today

1 _____

2 _____

3 _____

4 _____

5 _____

5 things i want to do in my life

1 _____

2 _____

3 _____

4 _____

5 _____

today's mantra

_____

this made me smile today:

_____

what i'm looking forward to tomorrow:

_____

i am grateful for:

_____

_____

_____

_____

_____

_____

5 things i need to do today

1 _____

2 _____

3 _____

4 _____

5 _____

5 things i want to do in my life

1 _____

2 _____

3 _____

4 _____

5 _____

today's mantra

_____

this made me smile today:

_____

what i'm looking forward to tomorrow:

_____

—— | —— | ——

i am grateful for:

_____

_____

_____

_____

_____

_____

5 things i need to do today

1 _____

2 _____

3 _____

4 _____

5 _____

5 things i want to do in my life

1 _____

2 _____

3 _____

4 _____

5 _____

today's mantra

_____

this made me smile today:

_____

what i'm looking forward to tomorrow:

_____

date

— | — | —

i am grateful for:

_____

_____

_____

_____

_____

_____

5 things i need to do today	*5 things i want to do in my life*
1 _____	1 _____
2 _____	2 _____
3 _____	3 _____
4 _____	4 _____
5 _____	5 _____

today's mantra

_____

this made me smile today:

_____

what i'm looking forward to tomorrow:

_____

date

___ | ___ | ___

i am grateful for:

_____

_____

_____

_____

_____

_____

5 things i need to do today

1 _____

2 _____

3 _____

4 _____

5 _____

5 things i want to do in my life

1 _____

2 _____

3 _____

4 _____

5 _____

today's mantra

_____

this made me smile today:

_____

what i'm looking forward to tomorrow:

_____

date

___ | ___ | ___

i am grateful for:

_____

_____

_____

_____

_____

_____

5 things i need to do today

1 _____

2 _____

3 _____

4 _____

5 _____

5 things i want to do in my life

1 _____

2 _____

3 _____

4 _____

5 _____

today's mantra

_____

this made me smile today:

_____

what i'm looking forward to tomorrow:

_____

—— | —— | ——

i am grateful for:

_____

_____

_____

_____

_____

_____

5 things i need to do today

1 _____

2 _____

3 _____

4 _____

5 _____

5 things i want to do in my life

1 _____

2 _____

3 _____

4 _____

5 _____

today's mantra

_____

this made me smile today:

_____

what i'm looking forward to tomorrow:

_____

—— | —— | ——

i am grateful for:

_____

_____

_____

_____

_____

_____

5 things i need to do today

5 things i want to do in my life

1 _____ 1 _____

2 _____ 2 _____

3 _____ 3 _____

4 _____ 4 _____

5 _____ 5 _____

today's mantra

_____

this made me smile today:

_____

what i'm looking forward to tomorrow:

_____

date

—— | —— | ——

i am grateful for:

_____

_____

_____

_____

_____

_____

5 things i need to do today   *5 things i want to do in my life*

1 _____   1 _____

2 _____   2 _____

3 _____   3 _____

4 _____   4 _____

5 _____   5 _____

today's mantra

_____

this made me smile today:

_____

what i'm looking forward to tomorrow:

_____

date

___ | ___ | ___

i am grateful for:

_____

_____

_____

_____

_____

_____

5 things i need to do today	*5 things i want to do in my life*
1 _____	1 _____
2 _____	2 _____
3 _____	3 _____
4 _____	4 _____
5 _____	5 _____

today's mantra

_____

this made me smile today:

_____

what i'm looking forward to tomorrow:

_____

— | — | —

i am grateful for:

_____

_____

_____

_____

_____

_____

5 things i need to do today | *5 things i want to do in my life*

1 _____ 1 _____

2 _____ 2 _____

3 _____ 3 _____

4 _____ 4 _____

5 _____ 5 _____

today's mantra

_____

this made me smile today:

_____

what i'm looking forward to tomorrow:

_____

date

___ | ___ | ___

i am grateful for:

_____

_____

_____

_____

_____

_____

5 things i need to do today

1 _____

2 _____

3 _____

4 _____

5 _____

5 things i want to do in my life

1 _____

2 _____

3 _____

4 _____

5 _____

today's mantra

_____

this made me smile today:

_____

what i'm looking forward to tomorrow:

_____

—— | —— | ——

i am grateful for:

_____

_____

_____

_____

_____

5 things i need to do today   *5 things i want to do in my life*

1 _____   1 _____

2 _____   2 _____

3 _____   3 _____

4 _____   4 _____

5 _____   5 _____

today's mantra

_____

this made me smile today:

_____

what i'm looking forward to tomorrow:

_____

date

—— | —— | ——

i am grateful for:

_____

_____

_____

_____

_____

_____

5 things i need to do today	*5 things i want to do in my life*
1 _____	1 _____
2 _____	2 _____
3 _____	3 _____
4 _____	4 _____
5 _____	5 _____

today's mantra

_____

this made me smile today:

_____

what i'm looking forward to tomorrow:

_____

date

— | — | —

i am grateful for:

_____

_____

_____

_____

_____

_____

5 things i need to do today

1 _____

2 _____

3 _____

4 _____

5 _____

5 things i want to do in my life

1 _____

2 _____

3 _____

4 _____

5 _____

today's mantra

_____

this made me smile today:

_____

what i'm looking forward to tomorrow:

_____

date

___ | ___ | ___

i am grateful for:

_____

_____

_____

_____

_____

_____

5 things i need to do today

1 _____

2 _____

3 _____

4 _____

5 _____

5 things i want to do in my life

1 _____

2 _____

3 _____

4 _____

5 _____

today's mantra

_____

this made me smile today:

_____

what i'm looking forward to tomorrow:

_____

i am grateful for:

_____

_____

_____

_____

_____

_____

5 things i need to do today

1 _____

2 _____

3 _____

4 _____

5 _____

5 things i want to do in my life

1 _____

2 _____

3 _____

4 _____

5 _____

today's mantra

_____

this made me smile today:

_____

what i'm looking forward to tomorrow:

_____

date

___ | ___ | ___

i am grateful for:

_____

_____

_____

_____

_____

_____

5 things i need to do today	*5 things i want to do in my life*
1 _____	1 _____
2 _____	2 _____
3 _____	3 _____
4 _____	4 _____
5 _____	5 _____

today's mantra

_____

this made me smile today:

_____

what i'm looking forward to tomorrow:

_____

there's no greater power

than knowing who you are.

—— | —— | ——

i am grateful for:

_____

_____

_____

_____

_____

_____

5 things i need to do today   *5 things i want to do in my life*

1 _____   1 _____

2 _____   2 _____

3 _____   3 _____

4 _____   4 _____

5 _____   5 _____

today's mantra

_____

this made me smile today:

_____

what i'm looking forward to tomorrow:

_____

date

—— | —— | ——

i am grateful for:

_____

_____

_____

_____

_____

_____

5 things i need to do today

1 _____

2 _____

3 _____

4 _____

5 _____

5 things i want to do in my life

1 _____

2 _____

3 _____

4 _____

5 _____

today's mantra

_____

this made me smile today:

_____

what i'm looking forward to tomorrow:

_____

date

—— | —— | ——

i am grateful for:

_____

_____

_____

_____

_____

_____

5 things i need to do today

1 _____

2 _____

3 _____

4 _____

5 _____

5 things i want to do in my life

1 _____

2 _____

3 _____

4 _____

5 _____

today's mantra

_____

this made me smile today:

_____

what i'm looking forward to tomorrow:

_____

date

___ | ___ | ___

i am grateful for:

_____

_____

_____

_____

_____

_____

5 things i need to do today   *5 things i want to do in my life*

1 _____   1 _____

2 _____   2 _____

3 _____   3 _____

4 _____   4 _____

5 _____   5 _____

today's mantra

_____

this made me smile today:

_____

what i'm looking forward to tomorrow:

_____

date

—— | —— | ——

i am grateful for:

_____

_____

_____

_____

_____

_____

5 things i need to do today

1 _____

2 _____

3 _____

4 _____

5 _____

5 things i want to do in my life

1 _____

2 _____

3 _____

4 _____

5 _____

today's mantra

_____

this made me smile today:

_____

what i'm looking forward to tomorrow:

_____

date

___ | ___ | ___

i am grateful for:

_____

_____

_____

_____

_____

_____

5 things i need to do today

1 _____

2 _____

3 _____

4 _____

5 _____

5 things i want to do in my life

1 _____

2 _____

3 _____

4 _____

5 _____

today's mantra

_____

this made me smile today:

_____

what i'm looking forward to tomorrow:

_____

date

—— | —— | ——

i am grateful for:

_____

_____

_____

_____

_____

_____

5 things i need to do today

1 _____

2 _____

3 _____

4 _____

5 _____

5 things i want to do in my life

1 _____

2 _____

3 _____

4 _____

5 _____

today's mantra

_____

this made me smile today:

_____

what i'm looking forward to tomorrow:

_____

date

___ | ___ | ___

i am grateful for:

_____

_____

_____

_____

_____

5 things i need to do today

1 _____

2 _____

3 _____

4 _____

5 _____

5 things i want to do in my life

1 _____

2 _____

3 _____

4 _____

5 _____

today's mantra

_____

this made me smile today:

_____

what i'm looking forward to tomorrow:

_____

date

___ | ___ | ___

i am grateful for:

_____

_____

_____

_____

_____

_____

5 things i need to do today

1 _____
2 _____
3 _____
4 _____
5 _____

5 things i want to do in my life

1 _____
2 _____
3 _____
4 _____
5 _____

today's mantra

_____

this made me smile today:

_____

what i'm looking forward to tomorrow:

_____

date

—— | —— | ——

i am grateful for:

_____

_____

_____

_____

_____

5 things i need to do today

1 _____

2 _____

3 _____

4 _____

5 _____

5 things i want to do in my life

1 _____

2 _____

3 _____

4 _____

5 _____

today's mantra

_____

this made me smile today:

_____

what i'm looking forward to tomorrow:

_____

date

—— | —— | ——

i am grateful for:

_____

_____

_____

_____

_____

_____

5 things i need to do today

1 _____

2 _____

3 _____

4 _____

5 _____

5 things i want to do in my life

1 _____

2 _____

3 _____

4 _____

5 _____

today's mantra

_____

this made me smile today:

_____

what i'm looking forward to tomorrow:

_____

date

—— | —— | ——

i am grateful for:

_____

_____

_____

_____

_____

_____

5 things i need to do today	*5 things i want to do in my life*
1 _____	1 _____
2 _____	2 _____
3 _____	3 _____
4 _____	4 _____
5 _____	5 _____

today's mantra

_____

this made me smile today:

_____

what i'm looking forward to tomorrow:

_____

date

―― | ―― | ――

i am grateful for:

_____

_____

_____

_____

_____

_____

5 things i need to do today	*5 things i want to do in my life*
1 _____	1 _____
2 _____	2 _____
3 _____	3 _____
4 _____	4 _____
5 _____	5 _____

today's mantra

_____

this made me smile today:

_____

what i'm looking forward to tomorrow:

_____

date

___ | ___ | ___

i am grateful for:

_____

_____

_____

_____

_____

_____

5 things i need to do today   *5 things i want to do in my life*

1 _____   1 _____

2 _____   2 _____

3 _____   3 _____

4 _____   4 _____

5 _____   5 _____

today's mantra

_____

this made me smile today:

_____

what i'm looking forward to tomorrow:

_____

date

—— | —— | ——

i am grateful for:

_____

_____

_____

_____

_____

_____

5 things i need to do today

1 _____

2 _____

3 _____

4 _____

5 _____

5 things i want to do in my life

1 _____

2 _____

3 _____

4 _____

5 _____

today's mantra

_____

this made me smile today:

_____

what i'm looking forward to tomorrow:

_____

date

—— | —— | ——

i am grateful for:

_____

_____

_____

_____

_____

_____

5 things i need to do today

1 _____

2 _____

3 _____

4 _____

5 _____

5 things i want to do in my life

1 _____

2 _____

3 _____

4 _____

5 _____

today's mantra

_____

this made me smile today:

_____

what i'm looking forward to tomorrow:

_____

date

—— | —— | ——

i am grateful for:

_____

_____

_____

_____

_____

_____

5 things i need to do today	*5 things i want to do in my life*
1 _____	1 _____
2 _____	2 _____
3 _____	3 _____
4 _____	4 _____
5 _____	5 _____

today's mantra

_____

this made me smile today:

_____

what i'm looking forward to tomorrow:

_____

date

___ | ___ | ___

i am grateful for:

_____

_____

_____

_____

_____

_____

5 things i need to do today	*5 things i want to do in my life*
1 _____	1 _____
2 _____	2 _____
3 _____	3 _____
4 _____	4 _____
5 _____	5 _____

today's mantra

_____

this made me smile today:

_____

what i'm looking forward to tomorrow:

_____

date

___ | ___ | ___

i am grateful for:

_____

_____

_____

_____

_____

_____

5 things i need to do today

1 _____

2 _____

3 _____

4 _____

5 _____

5 things i want to do in my life

1 _____

2 _____

3 _____

4 _____

5 _____

today's mantra

_____

this made me smile today:

_____

what i'm looking forward to tomorrow:

_____

date

___ | ___ | ___

i am grateful for:

_____

_____

_____

_____

_____

_____

5 things i need to do today

1 _____

2 _____

3 _____

4 _____

5 _____

5 things i want to do in my life

1 _____

2 _____

3 _____

4 _____

5 _____

today's mantra

_____

this made me smile today:

_____

what i'm looking forward to tomorrow:

_____

239

Love yourself when you fuck up,
when you make mistakes or
when you talk too much.

Love yourself when you lose your way,
when you react to things that
don't deserve your attention,
or you forget your intentions.

Love your shadows,
your wounds, and especially the
things you don't want to see.

Love all of it.

✦ *acknowledgments*

I would like to express my gratitude to the following people who made this book possible.

To my Spirit Daughter Team, thank you for your support, encouragement, and belief in my knowledge. I couldn't do any of this without you. Your dedication to our mission means the world to me.

Special thanks to Rebecca Reitz for her detail, precision, and talent. Your illustrations and sparkles throughout this book light up the content. You are the perfect match for my writing. Thank you for being the yin to my yang.

Thank you to my teacher, Diana Vitarelli, for giving me the seeds of this practice so many years ago. I am honored to nourish them and give them to the world through this book.

And Thank you to my husband for his willingness to listen to my hopes and dreams even in the wee hours of the morning. Thank you for reminding me of my strength and nudging me to always listen to myself. Our life together is proof that magic exists.

about the author ✦

Jill Wintersteen is the founder of Spirit Daughter, the popular astrology and wellness brand created to help you manifest your best life. Jill was introduced to astrology as a teenager and continued her exploration while studying yoga, meditation, and Chinese medicine. These practices served as the foundation of her life for over twenty years, even as Jill became a neuroscience researcher with a Master's Degree in Psychology. Realizing her true purpose for understanding consciousness was through spreading the messages of astrology, she began writing and distributing monthly workbooks with the Moon as her guide. Spirit Daughter's Moon Workbooks reach thousands of people worldwide each month, providing them insights to manifest their dreams while working with the energy of the Universe. The practices in this book are part of Jill's morning ritual and have guided her daily life as she rides the cycles of the Moon. To reach even more people, Jill shares inspirational messages to her community of over a million followers on Instagram through @spiritdaughter.

Thank the many versions of yourself that completed this journey and know that gratitude changes everything.